My big bumper
blue 1000 stickers

This activity book breaks into two fun sections! The first half is bursting with exciting sticker activities. The second half is full of cool doodling activities. Pull out the sticker sheets and have them with you when you complete the sticker pages. There are also lots of extra stickers to use anywhere you want!

Dinosaur differences

Use your stickers to complete the scene.

Explore the island, then find and circle the 6 differences between the two pictures.

3

Dinosaur park

Match the stickers to the dino scene!

PARASAUROLOPHUS
Par-a-SORE-owe-loaf-uss

STEGOSAURUS
STEG-owe-SORE-uss

Shhhh . . .
we are hiding
in the cave!

Sticker some
more small
dinosaurs here!

PTERODACTYL
Ter-owe-DAC-til

VELOCIRAPTOR
Vel-O-si-RAP-tor

TRICERATOPS
Try-SERRA-tops

SPINOSAURUS
Spy-no-SORE-uss

TYRANNOSAURUS REX
Tie-RAN-owe-SORE-uss-REX

5

Draw a crazy dinosaur here!

6

Buried bones!

Find the 12 bones hidden in the dino scene.

T rex terror!

Copy and colour the T rex then add some sticker teeth and an eye!

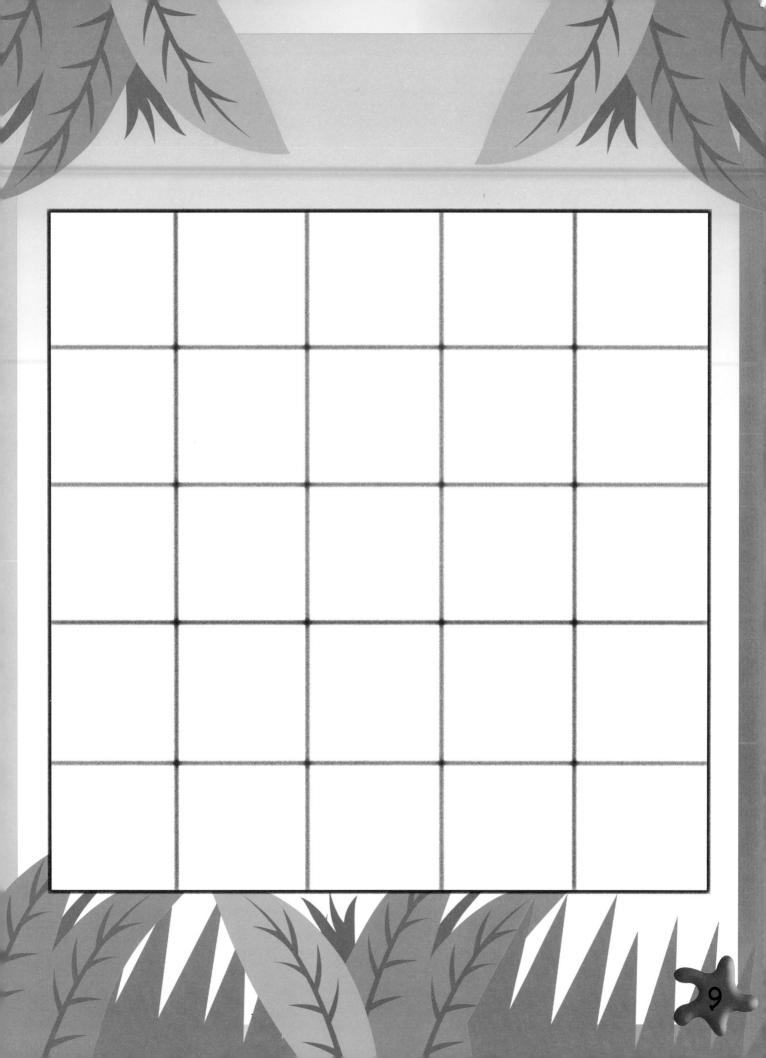

Then design
your own flag.

Get ready for **lift off!**

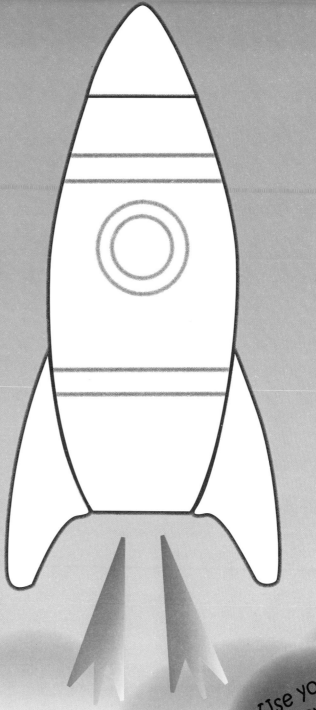

Use your stickers to complete the rocket and put some stars in the sky!

It's time to **explore** space!

Complete the scene with rockets, stars and aliens!

13

Space race!

Sticker the spaceships then guess which one lands on the moon!

14

Space exploration

This is a new planet that has just been discovered. Add stickers and your own designs to make it an exciting place to visit!

beep! beep!

glug!

boop!

Alien invaders!

Sticker 7 aliens onto the space station
then guide the spaceman to his rocket.
Will he make it without meeting any aliens?

Start here!

Practise drawing spaceships here!

Fun fish!

Join the dots to reveal
two big fun fish!

Colour in the fish and give them sticker eyes.

Fish hide and seek

Find and sticker the 8 hidden fish!

Help! Sharks!

Practise drawing
sharks here!

Leaping dolphins!

Join the dots and colour in the dolphins.
Then add some sticker splashes!

Counting jellyfish!

Use your sticker answers to complete the jellyfish number puzzles!

How many jellyfish are there in each box?

Sticker answer here!

Sticker answer here!

Sticker answer here!

Shark attack!
Fill the scene with fish and sharks!

24

Picnic pests

Match the shapes with your stickers to find out who's eating the food at the picnic.

Add more bug stickers!

Find stickers to match the shapes!

Spider trap!

Draw a big spider at the end of the web then match the stickers to find out who's been caught!

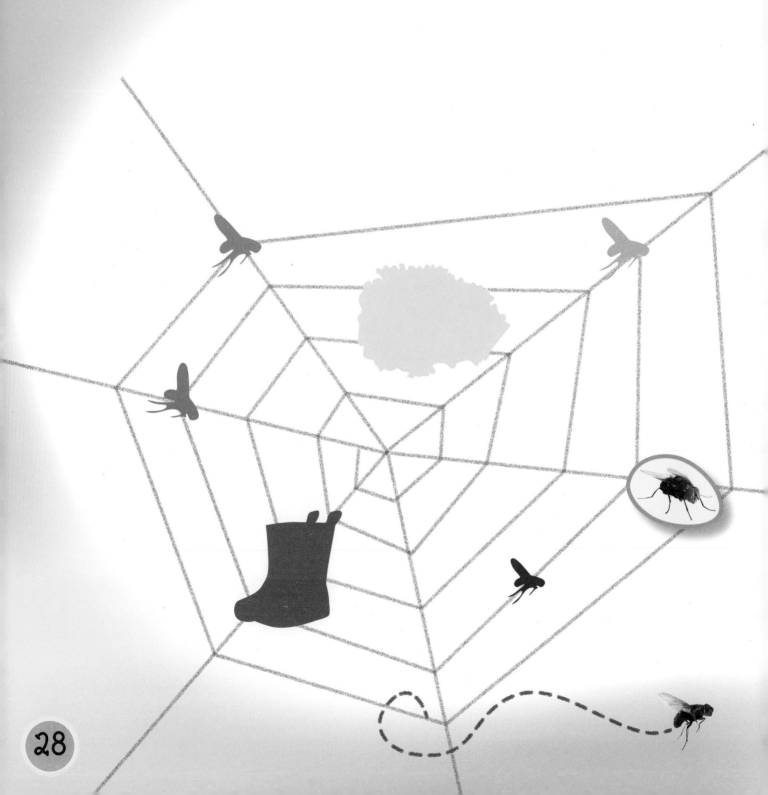

Design a bug!

We have given you its legs and its head — now you do the rest!

Spot the ball!

Find and sticker the 8 sports balls.

Ten-pin bowling

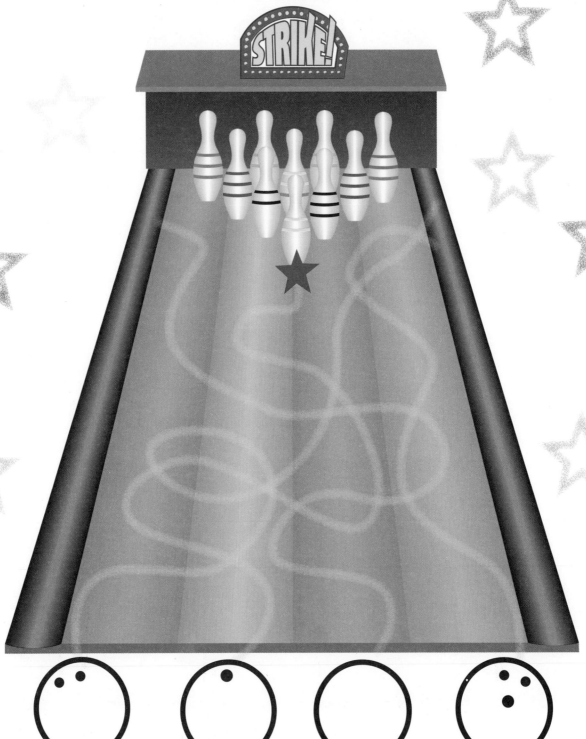

Match the stickers to the bowling balls then guess which one scores a strike!

32

Olympic runners!

Become a sports star in this exciting race for two or more players!

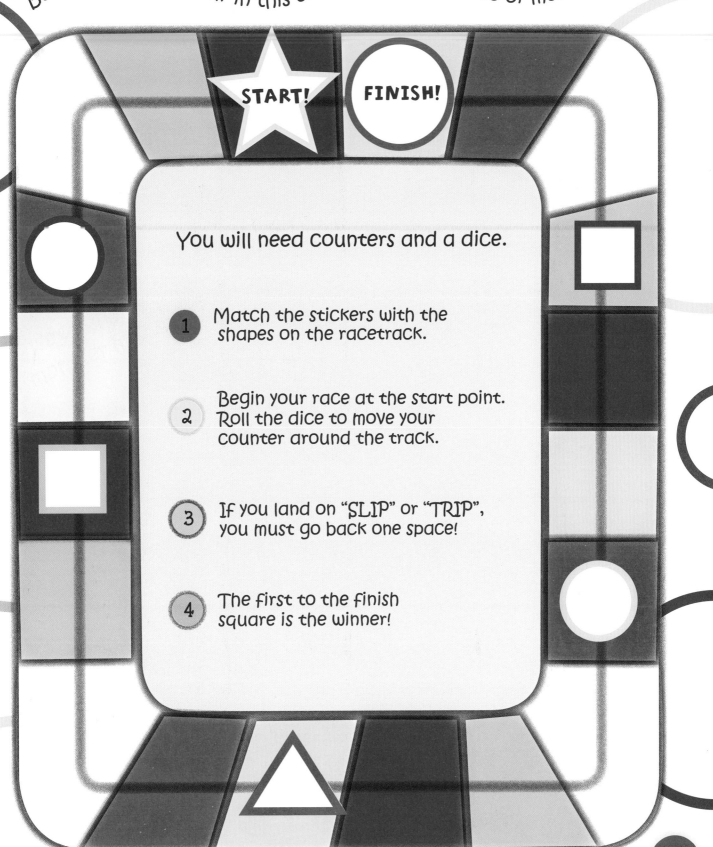

START!

FINISH!

You will need counters and a dice.

1. Match the stickers with the shapes on the racetrack.

2. Begin your race at the start point. Roll the dice to move your counter around the track.

3. If you land on "SLIP" or "TRIP", you must go back one space!

4. The first to the finish square is the winner!

What can you see out of the window?

I can see 1 ....**ar**....

I can see 2 ....**gs**....

I can see 3 ..**trees**..

Find the missing stickers!

BEEP!

34

Get packing!

Sticker two items for each of the suitcases.

Things to wear

Things to eat

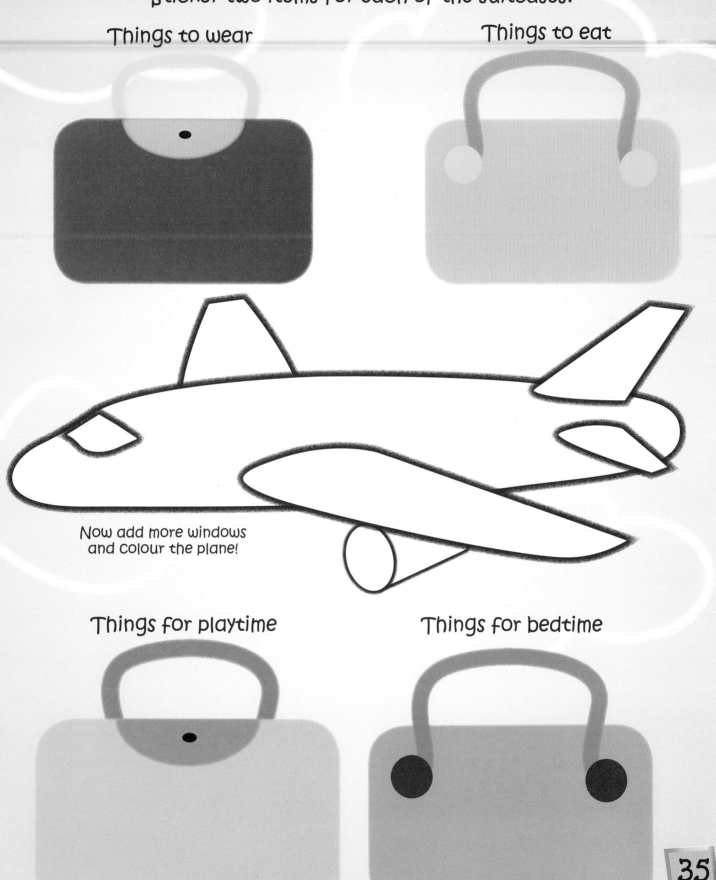

Now add more windows and colour the plane!

Things for playtime

Things for bedtime

35

Colour in your own racing car!

Join the dots to complete the sports car then add stripes, stickers and your own designs!

Colour the traffic lights!

Odd one out!

Match the stickers, then find the odd one out in each row of vehicles.

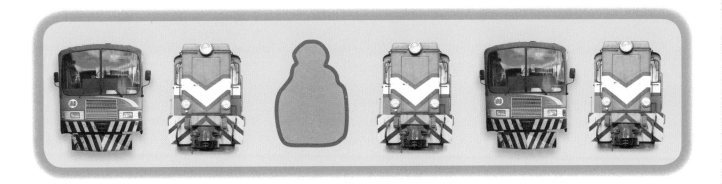

Practise drawing machines here!

38

Transport pairs

Complete the picture with your stickers then match the pairs with a straight line.

1) Find two sports cars.

2) Find two emergency vehicles.

3) Find two green vehicles.

4) Find two farm vehicles.

Scrapyard challenge

These broken vehicles need fixing! Find the matching parts then join them with a wiggly line.

Job List

Every time you mend a broken vehicle, find its sticker and complete the list.

Tractor

Car

Truck

Aeroplane

Stickers for page 2

Stickers for pages 4 & 5

Stickers for page 9

Stickers for pages 10 & 11

Stickers for pages 12 & 13

Stickers for page 14

Stickers for page 15

Stickers for pages 16 & 17

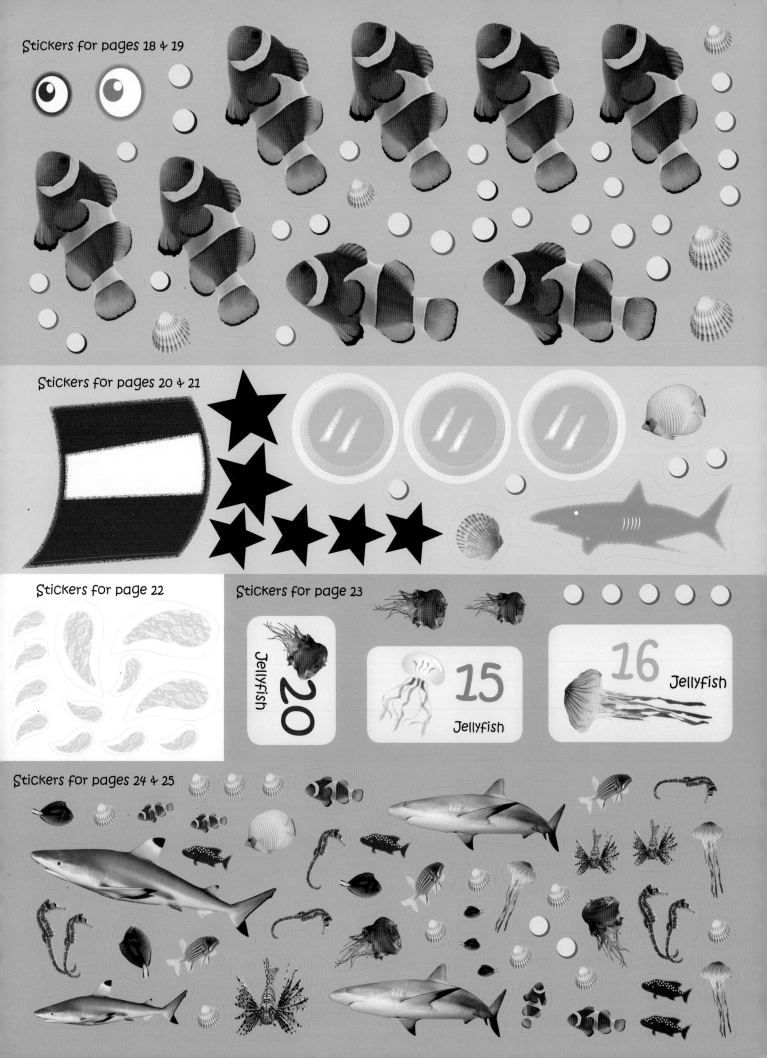

Stickers for pages 18 & 19

Stickers for pages 20 & 21

Stickers for page 22

Stickers for page 23

Jellyfish 20

15
Jellyfish

16
Jellyfish

Stickers for pages 24 & 25

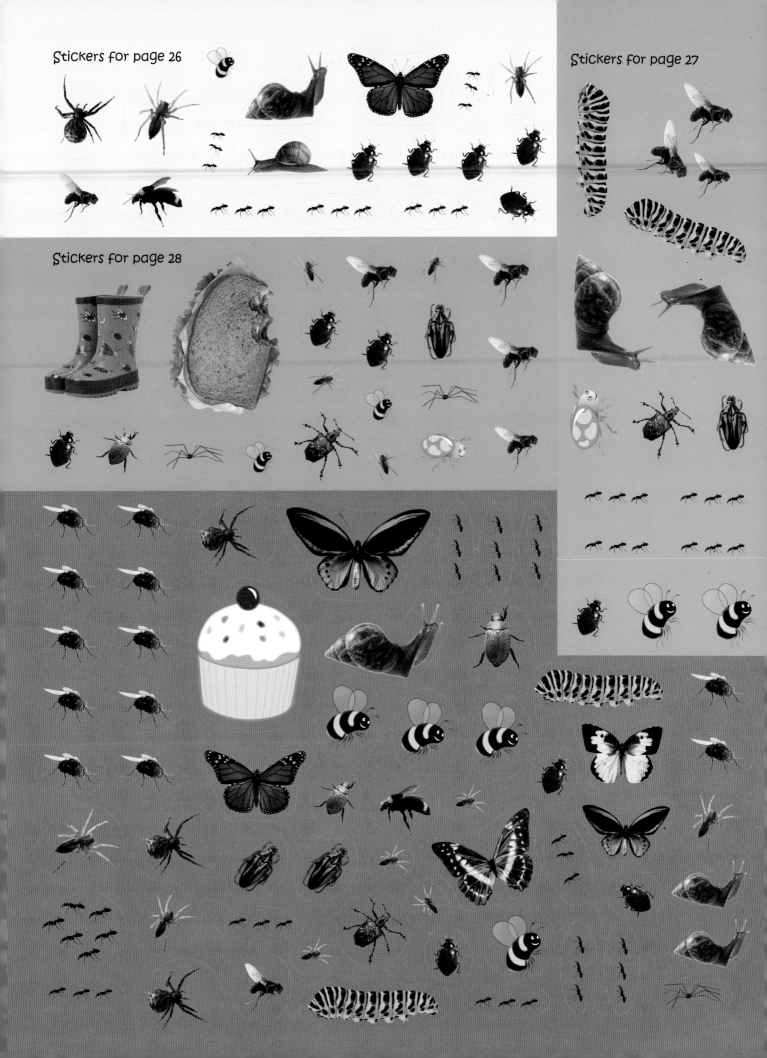

Stickers for page 26

Stickers for page 27

Stickers for page 28

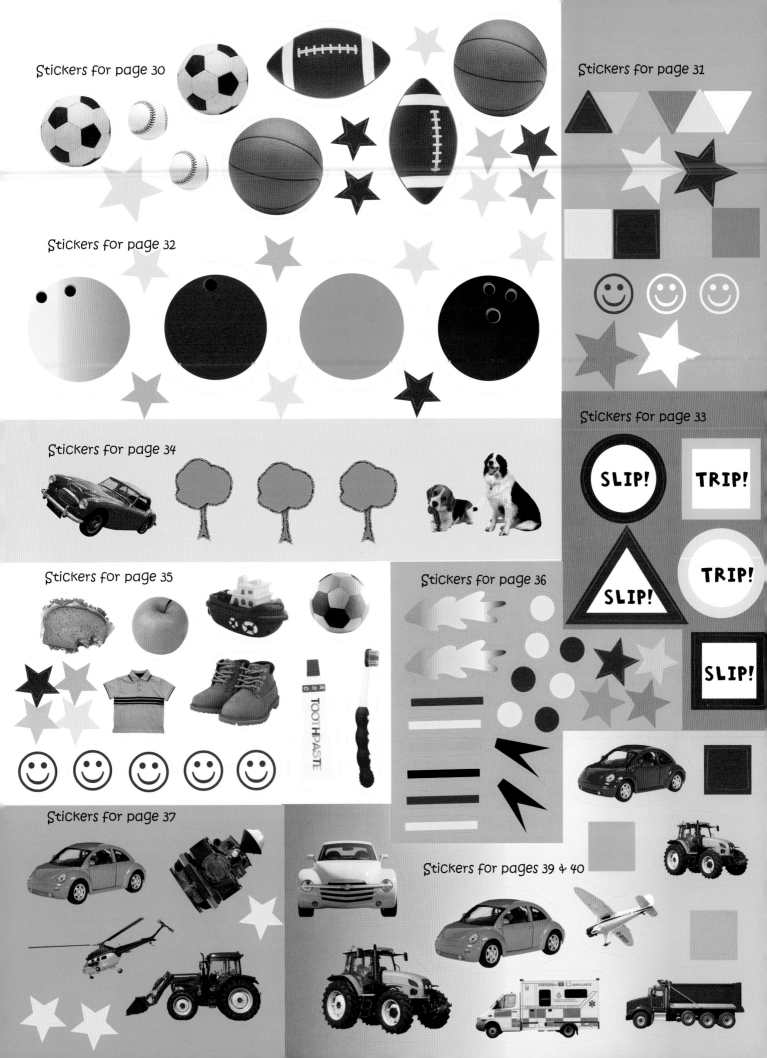

Stickers for page 30

Stickers for page 31

Stickers for page 32

Stickers for page 33

Stickers for page 34

Stickers for page 35

Stickers for page 36

Stickers for page 37

Stickers for pages 39 & 40

SLIP!

TRIP!

SLIP!

TRIP!

SLIP!

TOOTHPASTE

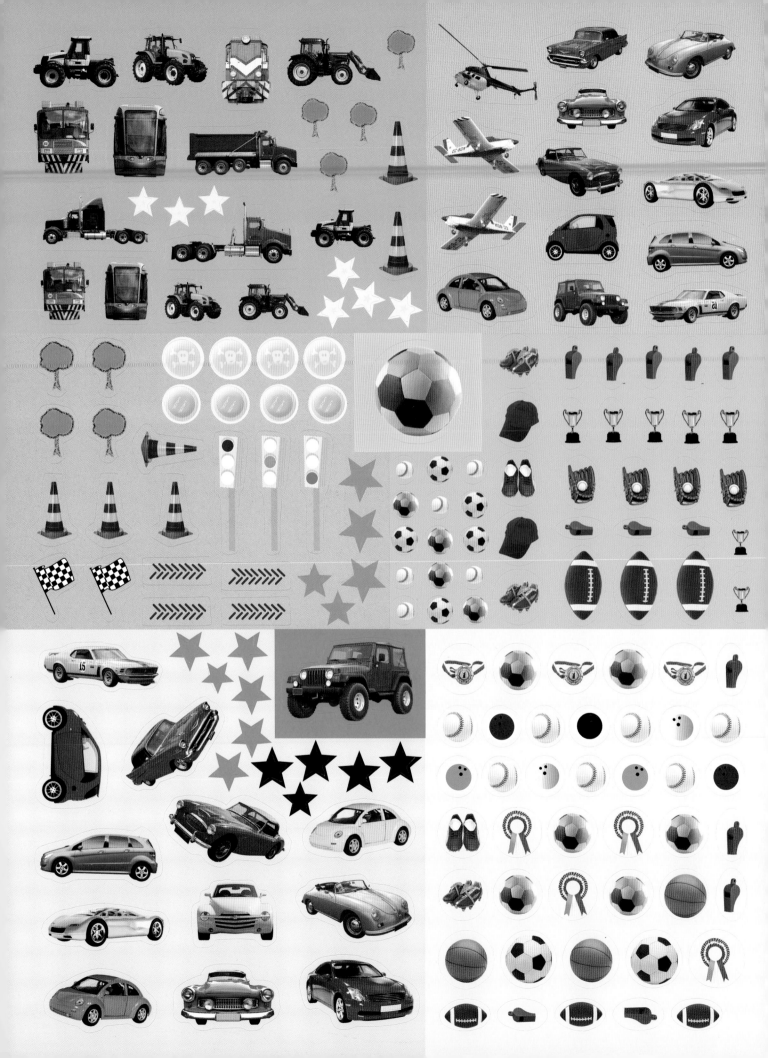

Busy bulldozer

Colour the bulldozer and then draw what is under the mud.

Fast fliers

Make these shapes into flying creatures!

Dinosaur country

Colour the dinosaur scene!

Pirate ship

Use the grid to copy the pirate ship and then add colour.

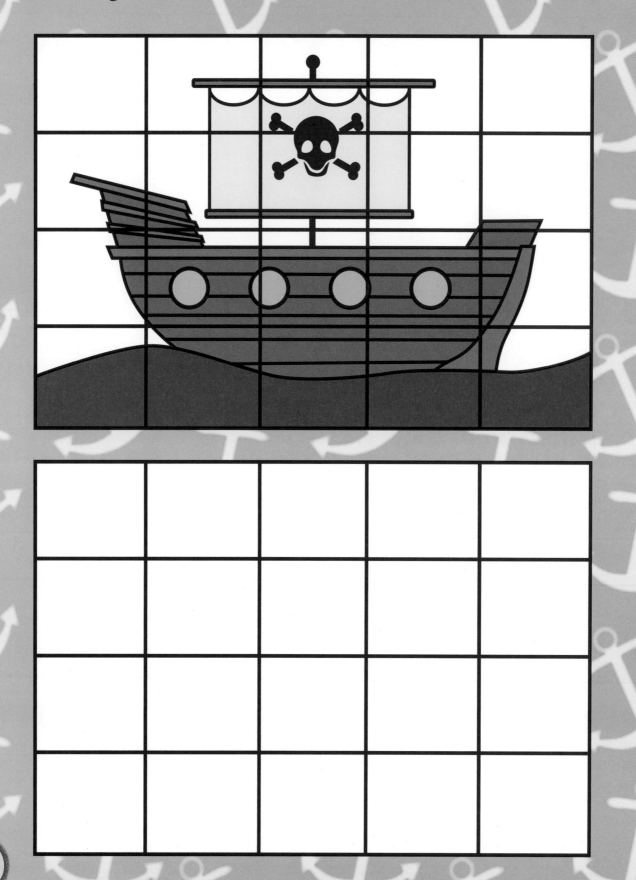

crazy pirate

Yarr!

Colour the crazy pirate
and his treasure!

King's castle

Which two shields are the same?

Draw a knight in the castle.

46

47

Robot doodles

Draw the missing half of the robot!

Monster madness!

Find your way through the monster maze!

Finish

Start

Colour these monsters.

49

Pirate wordsearch!

Find and circle the pirate words.
Words can be found across, up, down and diagonally!

T	R	E	A	S	U	R	E	T	O	N	
Q	C	R	C	P	S	R	N	E	T	I	
B	U	S	B	N	K	A	B	L	C	O	
R	N	H	M	F	U	D	O	E	W	C	
C	P	I	R	S	L	S	R	S	T	O	
M	A	P	Z	Q	L	A	W	C	M	D	
O	G	P	Z	H	T	C	G	O	Z	R	
H	O	O	K	R	U	E	N	P	R	J	
G	S	H	A	R	K	Y	Y	E	T	D	

1. Map
2. Flag
3. Treasure
4. Hook
5. Telescope

6. Skull
7. Shark
8. Sword
9. Coin
10. Ship

Shiver me timbers!

Draw somebody walking the plank!

Sports star!

Draw yourself playing your favourite sport.

Let's play!

Draw the rest of the crowd.

Design some banners.

Doodle who's playing baseball.

Ready, steady, race!

Zoom!

Start

Follow the maze to get to the finish line.

Finish

Trophy cabinet

1st 2nd 3rd

No.1

Design your own trophies!

BEST EVER!

Desert doodles

Who lives here?

Make the shapes into animals that hiss!

Silly pets!

Clockwork tortoise!

Add your own weird creations!

Long-legged cat!

Dinosaur shapes!

Roar!

Make the shapes into silly dinosaurs!

3, 2, 1, blast off!

Colour the rocket!

Who goes there?

Join the dots to reveal the creature!

61

Pizza wordsearch

Find and circle the pizza words. Words can be found across, down, up, diagonally, and backwards!

Fill the bowl with spaghetti!

T	U	N	A	E	W	E	O	S
C	X	D	L	O	S	Y	T	A
O	L	I	V	E	S	N	A	U
K	R	N	E	U	M	O	M	C
M	A	H	S	F	T	I	O	E
V	C	B	P	J	G	N	T	H
P	E	P	P	E	R	O	N	I

1. Sauce
2. Ham
3. Olives
4. Cheese
5. Tuna
6. Onion
7. Tomato
8. Pepperoni

Snack time!

Colour the food on the fork.

Fill the vending machine!

Smiling sharks!

Colour the three shark friends.

64

Pirate pictures

Draw the missing parts of these pirate outlaws!

To the rescue!

Draw a superhero to save the day!

Help!

66

Big catch!

What has been caught on the hook?

Draw a big starfish on the rock.

Wild, wild west!

Draw the missing half of the sheriff!

WANTED

Wanted gallery

One-eyed Jeff.

WANTED

Fill the posters and add colour!

£10,000

REWARD

WANTED

_____

_____

£1,000,000

REWARD
£1,000,000

Penguin Pete WANTED £50,000

Colour the bus!

Draw people on the bus.

Make this shape into a train!

Crazy cars!

Draw cars from the future.

Flying car!

Springy car!

Join the dots to find out who else lives here.

Roar!

73

Ahoy there!

Finish the crew.

Look out! Pirates!

Yarr!

Who is looking out of the portholes?

Tasty burger!

Use the grid to copy the burger and then add colour!

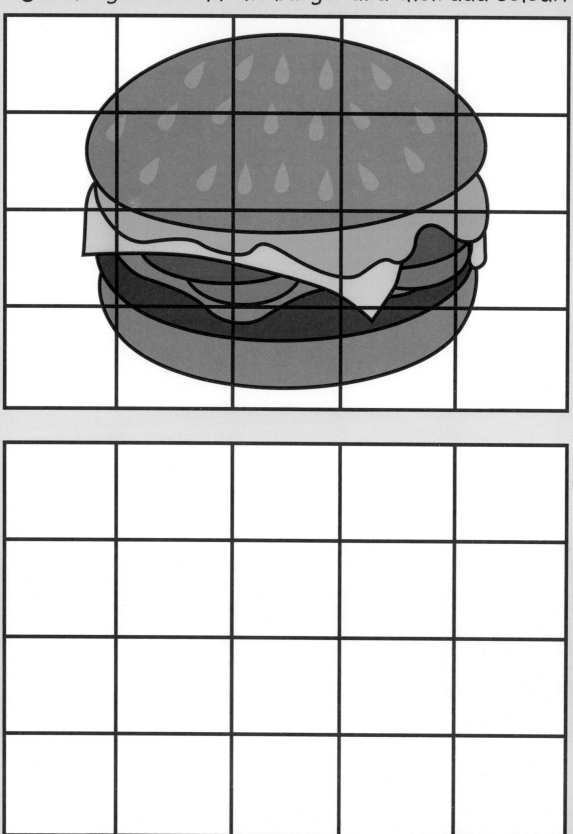

Munching mice

Follow the lines to see
who gets the cheese!

Eeeeeeeeeek!

Munch!

What is nibbling the chips?

Space secrets

Create a top-secret flying machine.

Start with this shape.

Heavy load

What is the plane lifting?

Colour quest!

Finish
and colour
the castle.